THE BIG BOOK OF ROCK

HAL LEONARD EUROPE
DISTRIBUTED BY MUSIC SALES

Exclusive Distributors:
Music Sales Limited
8/9 Frith Street, London W1D 3JB, England.
Music Sales Pty Limited
120 Rothschild Avenue, Rosebery, NSW 2018, Australia.

Order No. HLE90002088
ISBN 1-84449-474-8
This book © Copyright 2004 by Hal Leonard Europe

Cover design by Fresh Lemon
Printed in the USA

Your Guarantee of Quality
As publishers, we strive to produce every book to the highest
commercial standards.The book has been carefully designed to minimise
awkward page turns and to make playing from it a real pleasure.
Throughout, the printing and binding have been planned to ensure a sturdy,
attractive publication which should give years of enjoyment.
If your copy fails to meet our high standards, please inform us and
we will gladly replace it.

www.musicsales.com

THE
BIG
BOOK
OF
ROCK

ALL RIGHT NOW

Words and Music by PAUL RODGERS
and ANDY FRASER

Moderately, with a strong beat

There she stood _____ in the
I took her home _____ to my

street _____ smil-ing from her head _____ to her feet. I said,
place _____ watch-ing ev-'ry move on her face. She said,

"Hey, what is this?" _____ Now ba-by, may-be may-be she's in need _ of a
"Look, what's your game _____ ba-by, are you tryin' to put me in

kiss. I said, "Hey, what's your name ba-by,
shame?" I said, "Slow, don't go so fast,

may-be we can see things the same. Now don't you wait _____ or
don't you think that love ____ can last?" She said, ____ "Love, Lord a-

hes-i-tate, _____ let's move ____ be-fore they raise the park-ing
bove, _____ now ____ you're tryin' to trick me in

rate." } All right now _____ ba-by, it's all ____
love." }

BAD CASE OF LOVING YOU

Words and Music by
JOHN MOON MARTIN

AMERICAN PIE

from THE NEXT BEST THING

Words and Music by
DON McLEAN

A long, long time a-go I can still re-mem-ber how that mu-sic used to make me smile. _____ And I knew if I had my chance that I could make those peo-ple dance and may-be they'd be hap-py _____ for a while.

day the mu-sic died. And they were sing-in'.

This-'ll be the day _ that I _ die. _

Additional Lyrics

2. Now for ten years we've been on our own,
   And moss grows fat on a rollin' stone
   But that's not how it used to be
   When the jester sang for the king and queen
   In a coat he borrowed from James Dean
   And a voice that came from you and me
   Oh and while the king was looking down,
   The jester stole his thorny crown
   The courtroom was adjourned,
   No verdict was returned
   And while Lenin read a book on Marx
   The quartet practiced in the park
   And we sang dirges in the dark
   The day the music died
   We were singin'... bye-bye... etc.

3. Helter-skelter in the summer swelter
   The birds flew off with a fallout shelter
   Eight miles high and fallin' fast,
   it landed foul on the grass
   The players tried for a forward pass,
   With the jester on the sidelines in a cast
   Now the half-time air was sweet perfume
   While the sergeants played a marching tune
   We all got up to dance
   But we never got the chance
   'Cause the players tried to take the field,
   The marching band refused to yield
   Do you recall what was revealed
   The day the music died
   We started singin'... bye-bye... etc.

4. And there we were all in one place,
   A generation lost in space
   With no time left to start again
   So come on, Jack be nimble, Jack be quick,
   Jack Flash sat on a candlestick
   'Cause fire is the devil's only friend
   And as I watched him on the stage
   My hands were clenched in fists of rage
   No angel born in hell
   Could break that Satan's spell
   And as the flames climbed high into the night
   To light the sacrificial rite
   I saw Satan laughing with delight
   The day the music died
   He was singin'... bye-bye... etc.

BACK IN THE U.S.S.R.

Words and Music by JOHN LENNON
and PAUL McCARTNEY

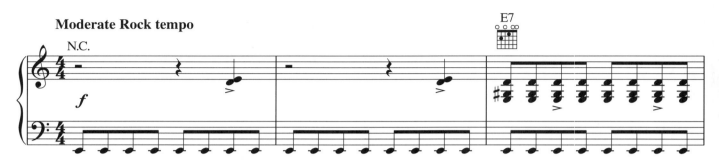

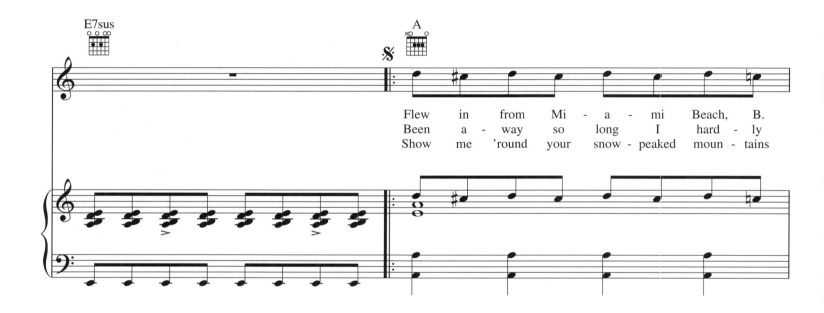

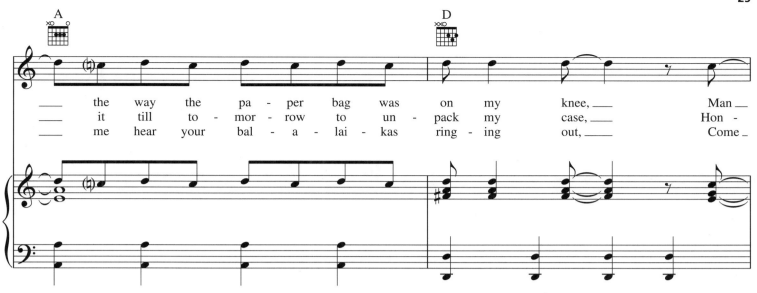

the way the pa - per bag was on my knee, ___ Man ___
it till to - mor - row to un - pack my case, ___ Hon -
me hear your bal - a - lai - kas ring - ing out, ___ Come ___

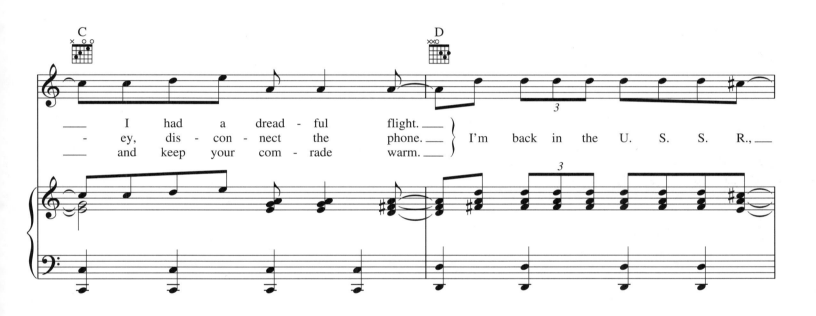

___ I had a dread - ful flight. ___
- ey, dis - con - nect the phone. } I'm back in the U. S. S. R., ___
___ and keep your com - rade warm. ___

To Coda

You don't __ know how luck - y you are, ___ boy. ___

BANG A GONG
(Get It On)

Words and Music by
MARC BOLAN

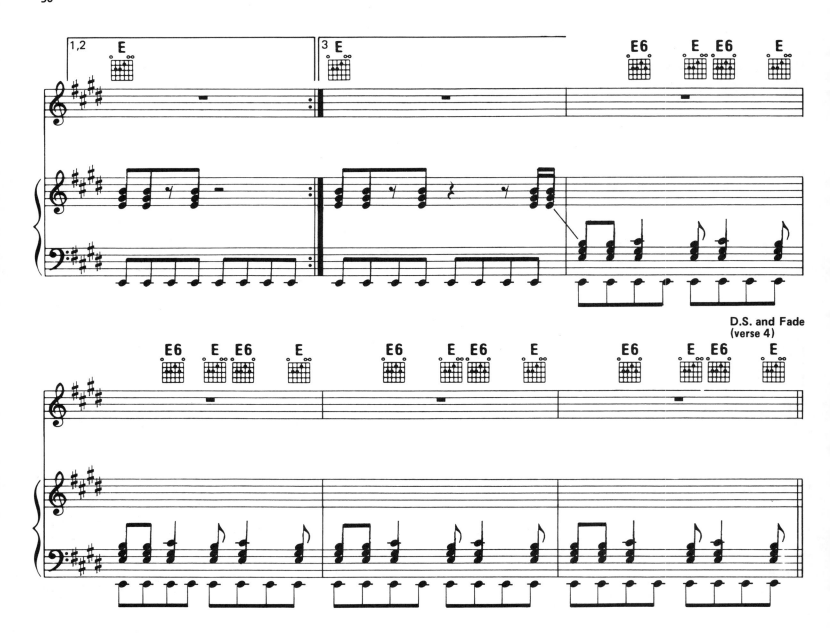

D.S. and Fade
(verse 4)

2. You're built like a car
   You've got a hub cap diamond star halo
   You're built like a car oh yeah
   You're an untamed youth that's the truth
   With your cloak full of eagles
   You're dirty sweet and you're my girl.

3. You're windy and wild
   You've got the blues in your shoes and your stockings
   You're windy and wild oh yeah
   You're built like a car
   You've got a hub cap diamond star halo
   You're dirty sweet and you're my girl.

4. You're dirty and sweet
   Clad in black, don't look back and I love you.
   You're dirty and sweet oh yeah
   You dance when you walk
   So let's dance, take a chance, understand me
   You're dirty sweet and you're my girl.

   To Chorus and Fade

BARRACUDA

Words and Music by ROGER FISHER,
NANCY WILSON, ANN WILSON and MICHAEL DEROSIER

Moderately fast

Sil - ly, sil - ly fools. _____

BEHIND BLUE EYES

Words and Music by
PETE TOWNSHEND

only lone - ly. _____ My love is ven - geance _____

that's nev - er free.

free. _____

When my fist clench - es, crack it o - pen ___

BORN TO BE WILD

from EASY RIDER

Words and Music by
MARS BONFIRE

Moderate Rock

Get your mo-tor run-ning. Head out on the high-way
I like smoke and light-ning, heav-y met-al thun-der

look-ing for ad-ven-ture in what
rac-ing in the wind and the

ev-er comes our way. Yeah, dar-ling, gon-na
feel-ing that I'm un-der.

THE BOYS ARE BACK IN TOWN

Words and Music by
PHIL LYNOTT

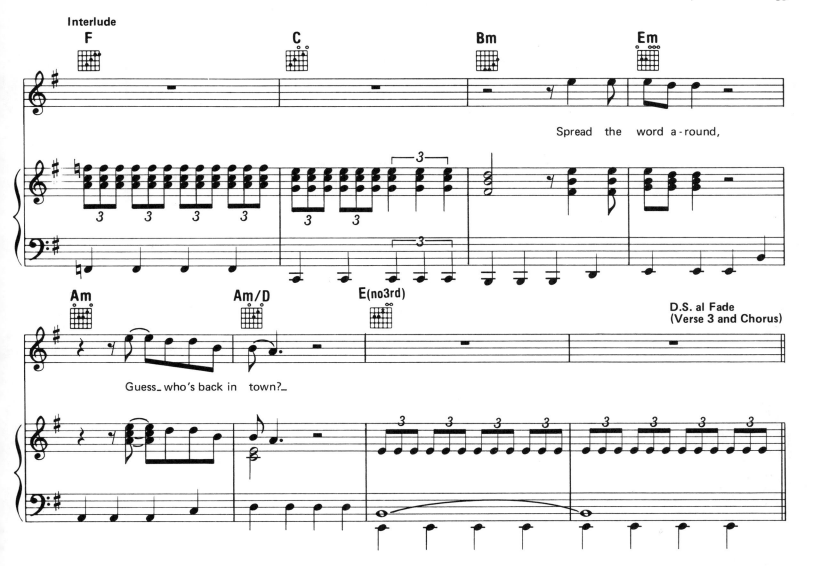

Interlude

Spread the word a-round,

Guess who's back in town?

D.S. al Fade
(Verse 3 and Chorus)

Additional Verses:

2. You know that chick that used to dance a lot
   Every night she'd be on the floor shaking what she'd got
   Man, when I tell you she was cool, she was hot
   I mean she was steaming.

   And that time over at Johnny's place
   Well, this chick got up and she slapped Johnny's face
   Man, we just fell about the place
   If that chick don't wanna know, forget her.

   (Chorus & Interlude)

3. Friday night they'll be dressed to kill
   Down at Dino's Bar and Grill
   The drink will flow and blood will spill
   And if the boys want to fight, you better let 'em

   That jukebox in the corner blasting out my favorite song
   The nights are getting warmer, it won't be long
   It won't be long till summer comes
   Now that the boys are here again.

   (Chorus and Fade)

BROWN EYED GIRL

Words and Music by
VAN MORRISON

Additional Lyrics

2. Whatever happened to Tuesday and so slow
   Going down the old mine with a transistor radio
   Standing in the sunlight laughing
   Hiding behind a rainbow's wall
   Slipping and a-sliding
   All along the water fall
   With you, my brown èyed girl
   You, my brown eyed girl.
   Do you remember when we used to sing:
   Chorus

3. So hard to find my way, now that I'm all on my own
   I saw you just the other day, my, how you have grown
   Cast my memory back there, Lord
   Sometime I'm overcome thinking 'bout
   Making love in the green grass
   Behind the stadium
   With you, my brown eyed girl
   With you, my brown eyed girl.
   Do you remember when we used to sing:
   Chorus

CELEBRATE

Words and Music by ALAN GORDON
and GARRY BONNER

Moderately slow, with a beat

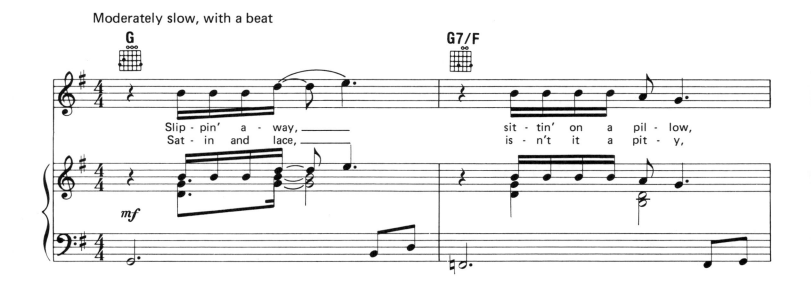

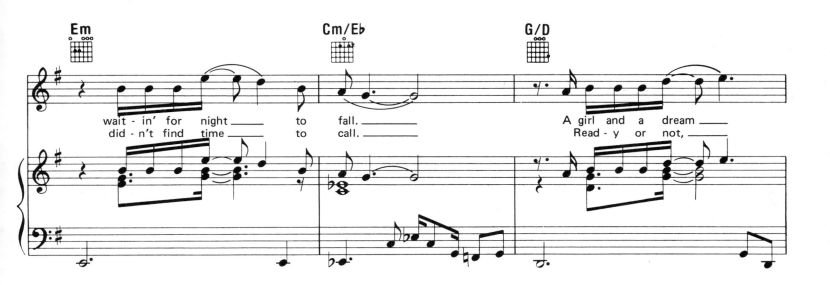

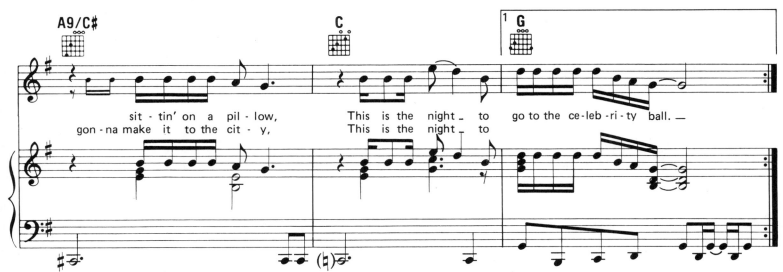

Lyrics:

Slip-pin' a - way, sit - tin' on a pil - low,
Sat - in and lace, is - n't it a pit - y,

wait - in' for night to fall.
did - n't find time to call.

A girl and a dream
Read - y or not,

sit - tin' on a pil - low,
gon - na make it to the cit - y,

This is the night to go to the ce-leb-ri-ty ball.
This is the night to

CALIFORNIA GIRLS

Words and Music by BRIAN WILSON
and MIKE LOVE

Medium Rock

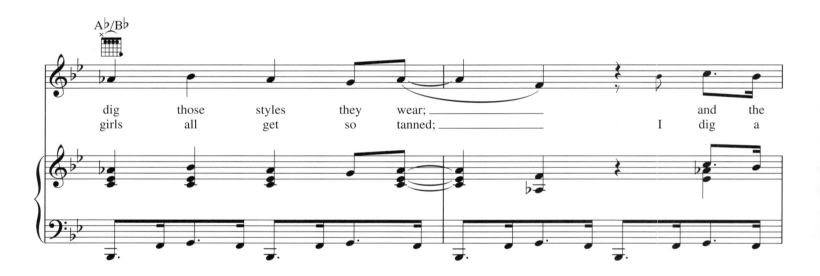

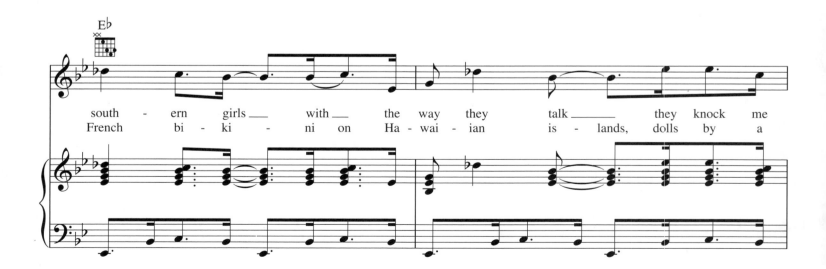

Repeat and Fade

CENTERFOLD

Written by
SETH JUSTMAN

Does she walk?__ Does she talk?__ Does she come com-plete?__ My
It's o-kay, __ I un-der-stand,__ this ain't no nev-er nev-er land. I

home-room, home-room an-gel al-ways pulled me from my seat
hope that when this is-sue's gone, I'll see you when your clothes are on.

CHANGES

Words and Music by
DAVID BOWIE

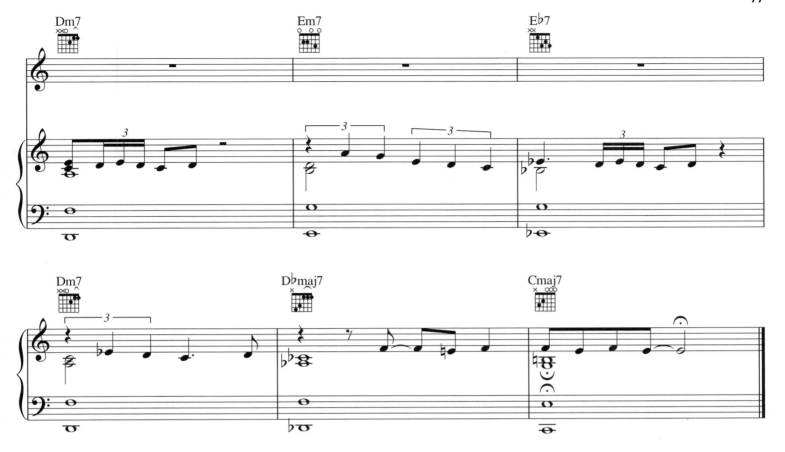

Additional Lyrics

2. I watch the ripples change their size, but never leave the stream
Of warm impermanence and so the days flowed through my eyes
But still the days seem the same.
And these children that you spit on as they try to change their worlds
Are immune to your consultations, they're quite aware of what they're going through.

(Ch-ch-ch-ch-Changes) Turn and face the strange.
(Ch-ch-changes) Don't tell them to grow up and out of it.
(Ch-ch-ch-ch-Changes) Turn and face the strange.
(Ch-ch-changes) Where's your shame? You've left us up to our necks in it.
Time may change me, but you can't trace time.

COME SAIL AWAY

Words and Music by
DENNIS DeYOUNG

CROCODILE ROCK

Words and Music by ELTON JOHN
and BERNIE TAUPIN

DON'T DO ME LIKE THAT

Words and Music by
TOM PETTY

(1.) I was talk-in' with a friend of mine, said a wom-an had hurt his pride.
(2., D.S.) Lis-ten hon-ey, can you see? Ba - by, it would bur - y me

DON'T FEAR THE REAPER

Words and Music by
DONALD ROESER

DREAMER

Words and Music by RICK DAVIES
and ROGER HODGSON

Lyrics:
you can do some-thing.) If I could do an-y-thing... (But can you do some-thing
out _____ of this world?) _____

Bb/C

C

Gm7/C
Take a dream on a Sun - day.

cresc. little by little

DON'T YOU
(Forget About Me)

Words and Music by KEITH FORSEY
and STEVE SCHIFF

Verse 2.

Don't you try and pretend,
It's my feeling, we'll win in the end.
I won't harm you, or touch your defenses,
Vanity, insecurity.
Don't you forget about me,
I'll be alone dancing, you know it, baby.
Going to take you apart,
I'll put us back together at heart, baby.

Don't you forget about me,
Don't, don't, don't, don't,
Don't you forget about me. *(To Coda)*

DREAMS

Words and Music by
STEVIE NICKS

GOODBYE YELLOW BRICK ROAD

Words and Music by ELTON JOHN
and BERNIE TAUPIN

Moderately slow, in 2

When are you gon-na come down   When are   you going   to land___
What do you think you'll do then   I bet that -'ll shoot down____   your plane____

___ I should have stayed __ on the farm____   Should have list -ened___ to my___ old man___
___ It -'ll take you a cou -ple of vod -ka and ton -ics to   set you on your feet a -gain___

___ You know you can't hold __ me for -ev -er ___   I did -n't sign up __ with you____
___ May -be you'll get __ a re -place -ment   there's plen -ty like me __ to be found___

EVERYBODY PLAYS THE FOOL, SOMETIME

Words and Music by RUDY CLARK,
KENNY WILLIAMS and J.R. BAILEY

FAITH

Words and Music by
GEORGE MICHAEL

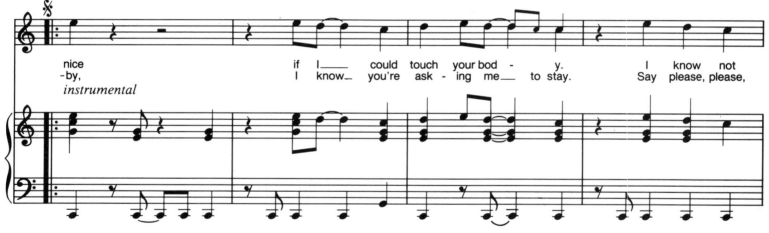

FREE BIRD

Words and Music by ALLEN COLLINS
and RONNIE VAN ZANT

Lord knows I can't change._____

(Instrumental)

Lord, help me, I can't change.

GIMME SOME LOVIN'

Words and Music by STEVE WINWOOD,
MUFF WINWOOD and SPENCER DAVIS

Moderately bright

Hey!

Well, my

tem - p'ra - ture's ris - ing and my feet on the floor.
feel so good; __ ev - 'ry - thing is sound - ing hot.
feel so good; __ ev - 'ry - bod - y's get - tin' high.

HANG ON SLOOPY

Words and Music by WES FARRELL
and BERT RUSSELL

A HARD DAY'S NIGHT

Words and Music by JOHN LENNON
and PAUL McCARTNEY

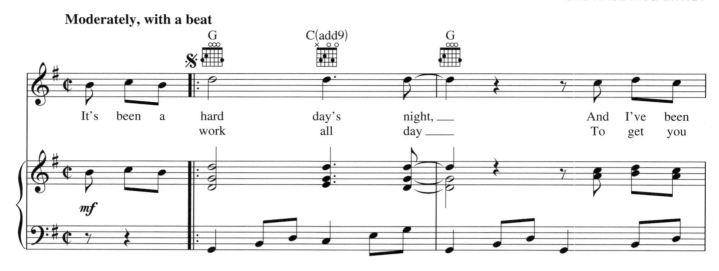

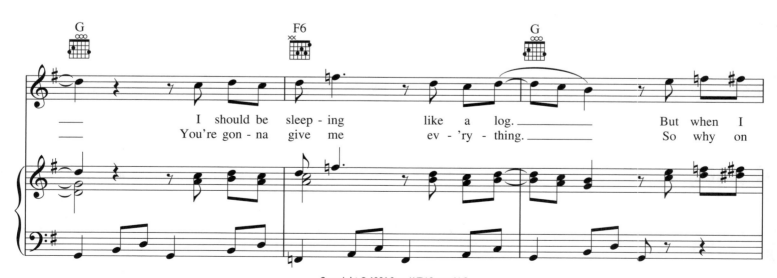

HIT ME WITH YOUR BEST SHOT

Words and Music by EDDIE SCHWARTZ

Moderate Rock

HEAVEN

Words and Music by BRYAN ADAMS
and JIM VALLANCE

Oh, think - in' a - bout ___ all our
Oh, once in your life ___ you will

young - er years; ___ there was on - ly you ___ and me; ___ we were
find some - one ___ who will turn your world ___ a - round; ___ bring you

HEY JUDE

Words and Music by JOHN LENNON
and PAUL McCARTNEY

I LOVE ROCK 'N ROLL

Words and Music by ALAN MERRILL
and JAKE HOOKER

I WANT TO KNOW WHAT LOVE IS

Words and Music by
MICK JONES

I'M JUST A SINGER
(In A Rock And Roll Band)

Words and Music by
JOHN LODGE

With a driving rhythm

Verse lyrics:

I'm just a wan-d'ring on the face of this earth, __ meet-ing so man-y peo-ple who are
A thou-sand pic-tures can be drawn from one word, __ on-ly who is the art-ist. We
Mu-sic is the trav-el-er __ cross-ing the world __ meet-ing so man-y peo-ple __

To Coda

try'n to be free, __ And while I'm trav'-lin' I hear so man-y words __ lan-guage
got-ta a-gree __ a thou-sand miles __ can lead so man-y ways __ Just to
bridg-ing the seas __

Dm

bar-ri-ers brok-en, now we've found __ the key. And if you want the wind of change to blow __
know who is driv-ing, what a help it would be __ So if you want this world of yours to turn __

see a fright-ened per-son who is fright-ened by the peo-ple who are scorch-ing this

earth,_____ scorch-ing this earth._____

We're just the sing-ers in a rock and roll band._

LAY DOWN SALLY

Words and Music by ERIC CLAPTON,
MARCY LEVY and GEORGE TERRY

There is noth - ing that __ is wrong __ in want - ing you __ to stay __
sun ain't near - ly on __ the rise, __ and we still got __ the moon __
long to see __ the morn - ing light __ col - or - ing __ your face __

__ here __ with me.
__ and stars __ a - bove.
__ so dream - i - ly.

I
So

JOY TO THE WORLD

Words and Music by
HOYT AXTON

KARMA CHAMELEON

Words and Music by GEORGE O'DOWD, JON MOSS,
MICHAEL CRAIG, ROY HAY and PHIL PICKETT

go

you come__ and go__

Lov-ing would be ea-sy if your col-ours were like__ my__

dream red gold and green

red gold and green.

Repeat and Fade

LADY MADONNA

Words and Music by JOHN LENNON
and PAUL McCARTNEY

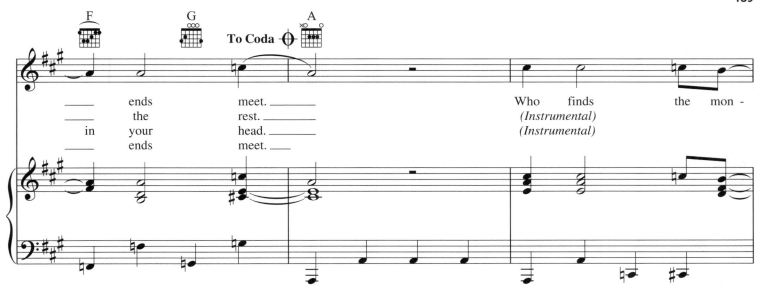

Who finds the mon-
(Instrumental)
(Instrumental)

___ ends meet. ___
___ the rest. ___
in your head. ___
___ ends meet. ___

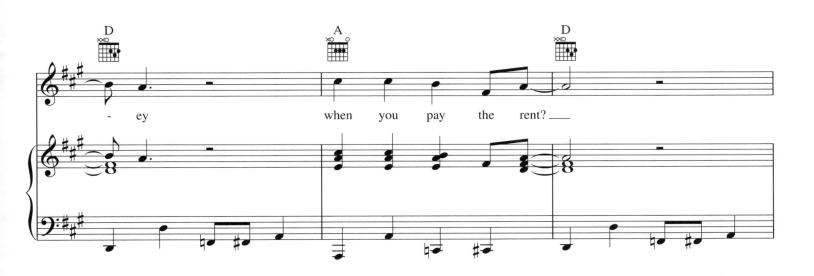

-ey when you pay the rent? ___

Did you think that mon-ey was ___ heav- en sent? ___

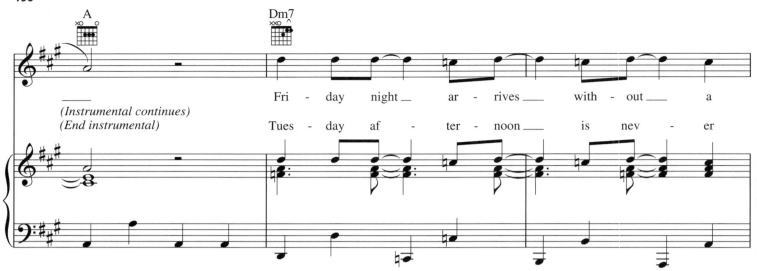

(Instrumental continues)
(End instrumental)

Fri - day night ___ ar - rives ___ with - out ___ a
Tues - day af - ter - noon ___ is nev - er

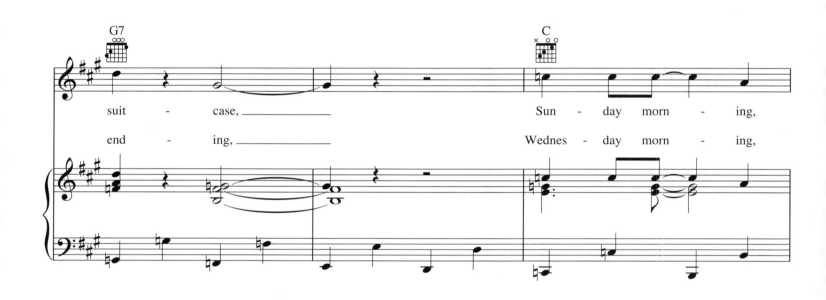

suit - case, _____
end - ing, _____

Sun - day morn - ing,
Wednes - day morn - ing,

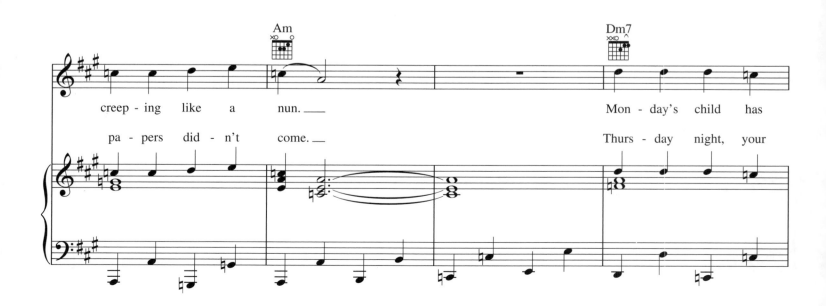

creep - ing like a nun. ___
pa - pers did - n't come. ___

Mon - day's child has
Thurs - day night, your

LAYLA

Words and Music by ERIC CLAPTON
and JIM GORDON

Original key: E♭ minor. This edition has been transposed up one whole-step to be more playable.

193

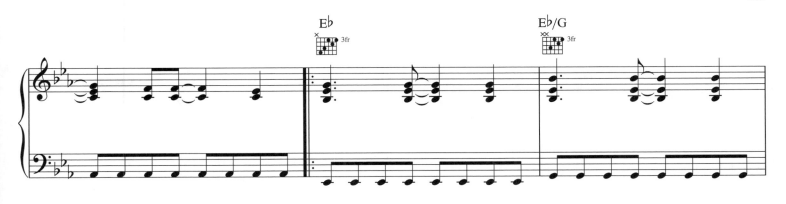

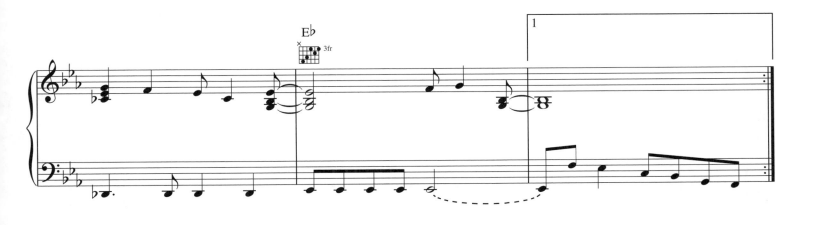

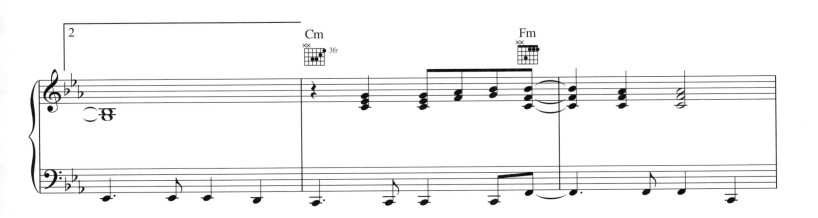

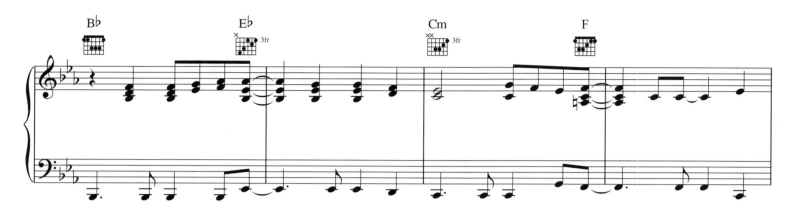

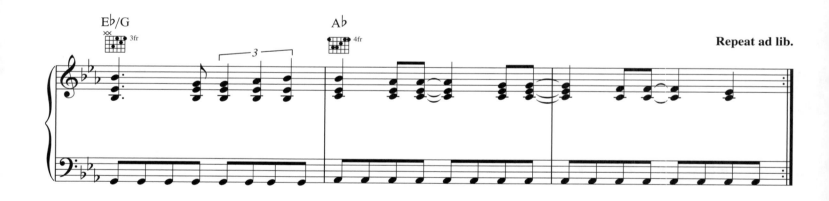

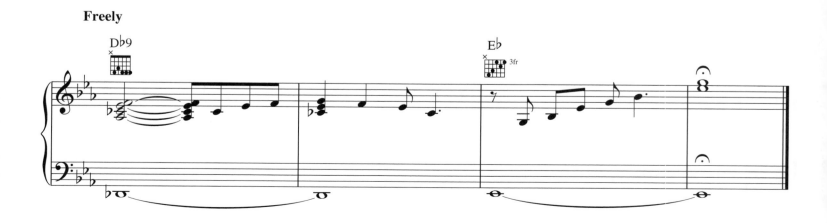

LONG TALL SALLY

Words and Music by ENOTRIS JOHNSON,
RICHARD PENNIMAN and ROBERT BLACKWELL

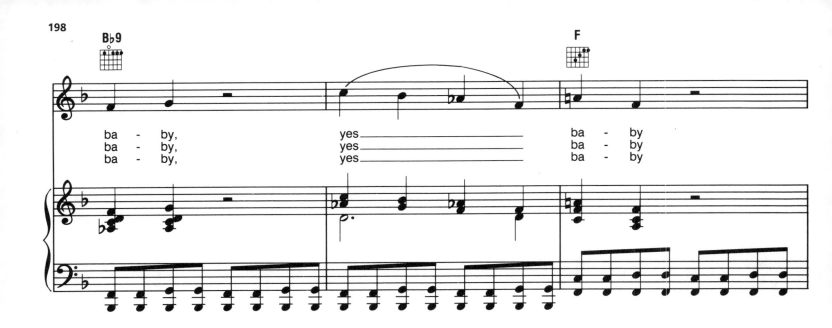

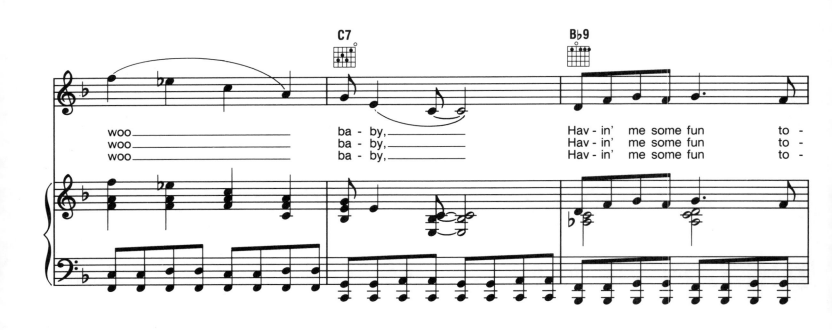

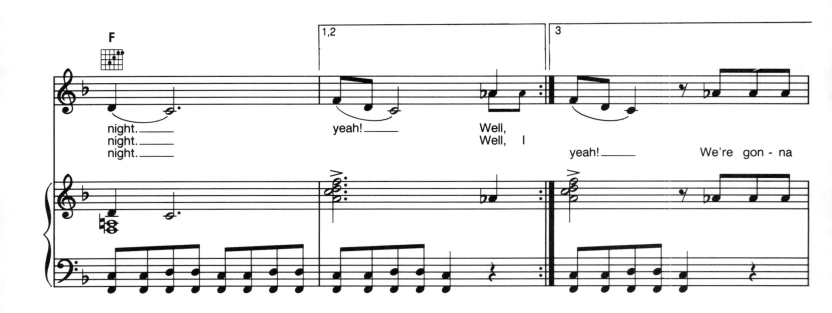

LIGHT MY FIRE

Words and Music by
THE DOORS

LIVIN' ON A PRAYER

Words and Music by DESMOND CHILD,
JON BON JOVI and RICHIE SAMBORA

Moderate Rock

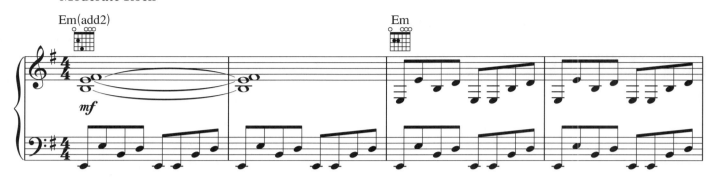

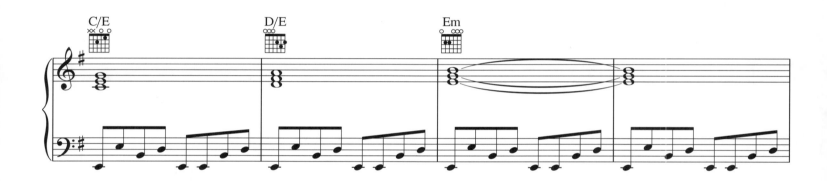

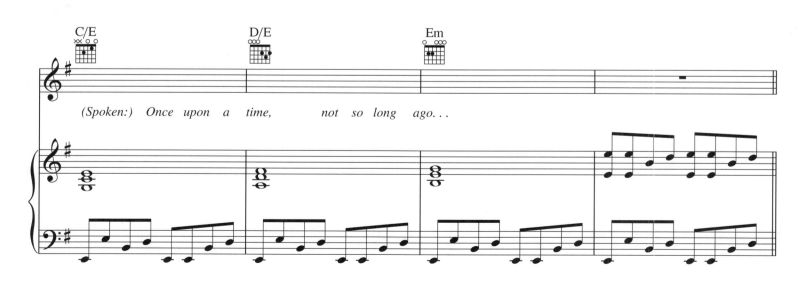

(Spoken:) Once upon a time, not so long ago...

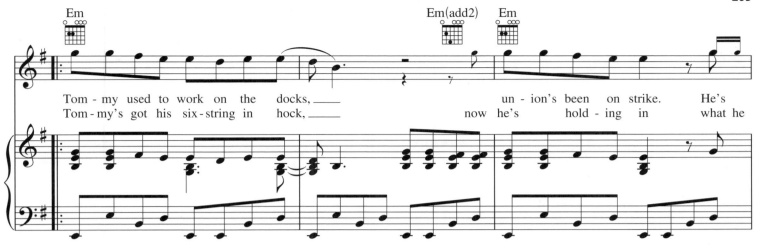

Tom - my used to work on the docks, _____ un - ion's been on strike. He's
Tom - my's got his six - string in hock, _____ now he's hold - ing in what he

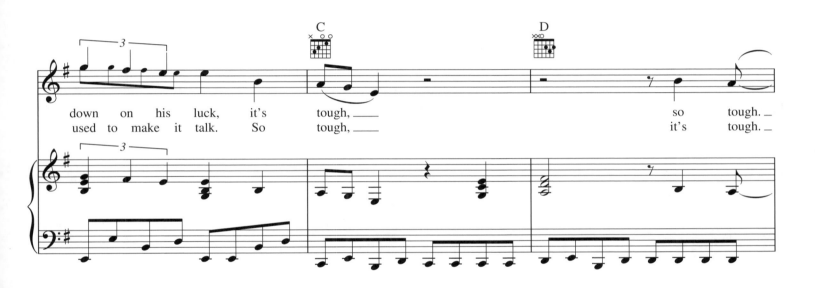

down on his luck, it's tough, _____ so tough. _
used to make it talk. So tough, _____ it's tough. _

_____ Gi - na works the di - ner all day _
_____ Gi - na dreams of run - ning a - way; _

LOUIE, LOUIE

Words and Music by
RICHARD BERRY

* Lyrics omitted at the request of the publisher.

MAGGIE MAY

Words and Music by ROD STEWART
and MARTIN QUITTENTON

Additional Lyrics

2. You lured me away from home, just to save you from being alone.
   You stole my soul, that's a pain I can do without.
   All I needed was a friend to lend a guiding hand.
   But you turned into a lover, and, Mother, what a lover! You wore me out.
   All you did was wreck my bed and in the morning kick me in the head.
   Oh, Maggie, I couldn't have tried any more.

3. You lured me away from home 'cause you didn't want to be alone.
   You stole my heart, I couldn't leave you if I tried.
   I suppose I could collect my books and get back to school,
   Or steal my Daddy's cue and make a living out of playing pool,
   Or find myself a rock and roll band that needs a helpin' hand.
   Oh, Maggie, I wish I'd never seen your face. *(To Coda)*

MONDAY, MONDAY

Words and Music by
JOHN PHILLIPS

Moderately

1,3. Mon - day, Mon - day, so good to me
2. Mon - day, Mon - day, Can't trust that day

Mon - day morn - in', it was all I hoped it would be.
Mon - day, Mon - day, some - times it just turns out that way.

Oh, Mon - day morn - in', Mon - day morn - in' could - n't guar - an - tee
Oh, Mon - day morn - in', you give me no warn - in' of what was to be

MORE THAN WORDS

Words and Music by NUNO BETTENCOURT
and GARY CHERONE

Say - in' "I ____ love ____ you" is
Now that I've ____ tried ____ to

not the words ____ I want ____ to ____ hear from you. ____ It's not that I ____
talk to you ____ and make ____ you un - der - stand, ____ all ____ you ____

Original key: F♯ major. This edition has been transposed up one half-step to be more playable.

MY SWEET LORD

Words and Music by
GEORGE HARRISON

NIGHTS IN WHITE SATIN

Words and Music by
JUSTIN HAYWARD

REELING IN THE YEARS

Words and Music by WALTER BECKER
and DONALD FAGEN

OWNER OF A LONELY HEART

Words and Music by TREVOR HORN, JON ANDERSON,
TREVOR RABIN and CHRIS SQUIRE

Move your-self.
Say you don't want to change it.
You al-ways live your life
nev-er think-ing of the fu-

You've been hurt so be-

-ture.
fore.

Prove your-self.
Watch it now,

You are the move you make.
the ea-gle in the sky,

Own - er of a lone - ly heart.__

PRIDE
(In The Name Of Love)

Lyrics by BONO
Music by U2

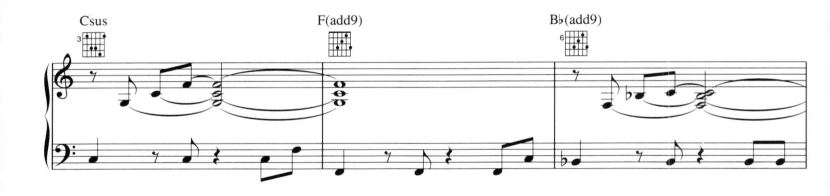

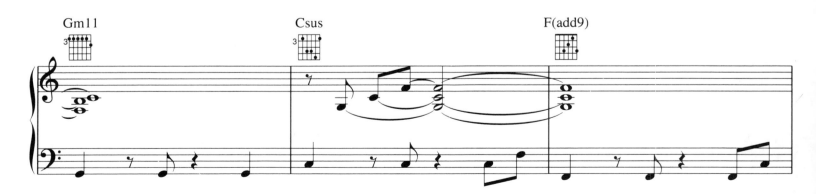

RADAR LOVE

Words and Music by GEORGE KOOYMANS
and BARRY HAY

I've been driv - in' all night. My hand's wet on the wheel.
ra - di - o was play - in' some for - got - ten song.
No more speed, I'm al - most there.

There's a voice ___ in my head ___ that
Bren - da Lee ___ is
I got - ta keep cool now, I

drives my heel. ___
com - in' on strong. ___
got - ta take care. ___

It's my ba -
The road ___
Last ___

- by call - in', said, "I need ___ you here." ___
___ has got ___ me hyp - no - tized. ___
___ car to pass, here ___ I go. ___

And it's half past four and I'm shift - in' gear. ___
And I'll be spit - ting in - to a new sun - rise. ___
And the line of cars drove down real slow. ___

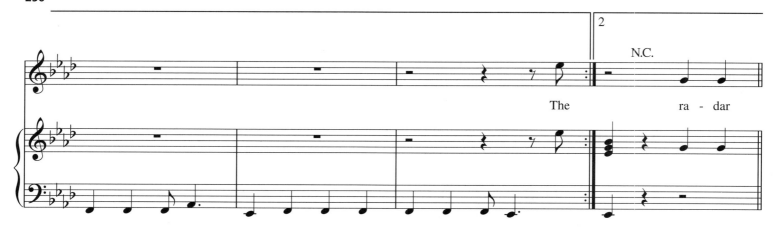

The ra - dar

Play 4 times

love. _

N.C.

ROCK AND ROLL HOOCHIE KOO

Words and Music by
RICK DERRINGER

ROCK AND ROLL IS HERE TO STAY

Words and Music by
DAVID WHITE

Rock and roll is here to stay, ___ it will nev - er die. ___
Rock and roll will al - ways be, ___ I dig it to the end. ___
If you don't like rock and roll, ___ think what you've been miss -

___ It was meant to be that way, ___
___ It - 'll go down in his - to - ry, ___
- in', _____ but if you like to bop and stroll, _

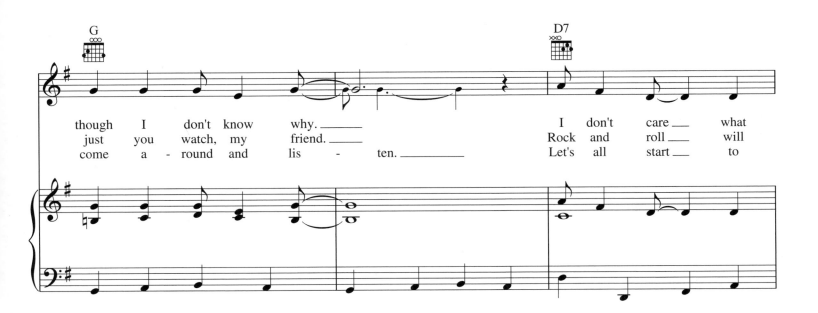

though I don't know why. _____ I don't care ___ what
just you watch, my friend. _____ Rock and roll ___ will
come a - round and lis - ten. _____ Let's all start ___ to

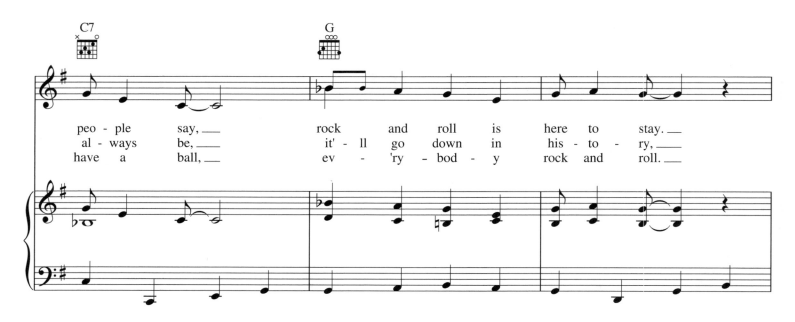

peo - ple say, ___ rock and roll is here to stay. ___
al - ways be, ___ it' - ll go down in his - to - ry, ___
have a ball, ___ ev - 'ry - bod - y rock and roll. ___

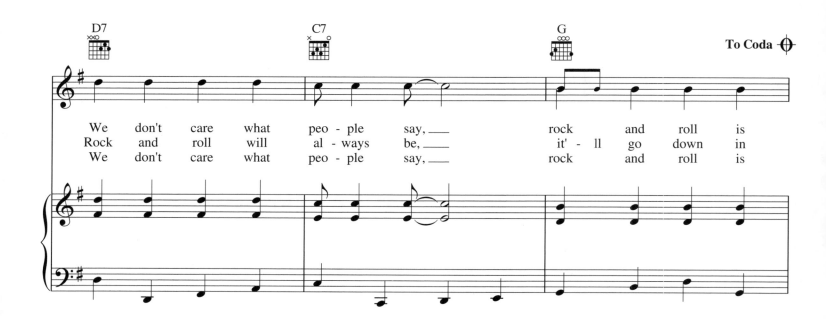

We don't care what peo - ple say, ___ rock and roll is
Rock and roll will al - ways be, ___ it' - ll go down in
We don't care what peo - ple say, ___ rock and roll is

To Coda ⊕

here to stay. ___ his - to - ry. ___ Ev - 'ry - bod - y

ROCK THE CASBAH

Words and Music by JOE STRUMMER,
MICK JONES and TOPPER HEADON

SHE WORKS HARD FOR THE MONEY

Words and Music by DONNA SUMMER
and MICHAEL OMARTIAN

SHOW ME THE WAY

Words and Music by
PETER FRAMPTON

I wonder how you're feel-ing. There's

I can see no rea-son. You're

SURFIN' U.S.A.

Words by BRIAN WILSON
Music by CHUCK BERRY

STILL THE SAME

Words and Music by
BOB SEGER

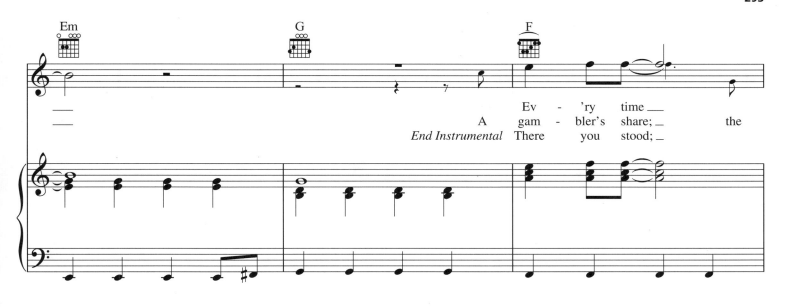

Ev - 'ry time ___
A gam - bler's share; ___ the
End Instrumental There you stood; ___

they were sure they had you caught, ___
on - ly risk that you would take, ___
ev - 'ry - bod - y watched you play. ___

you were quick - er than they thought. ___
the on - ly loss you could for - sake, ___
I just turned and walked a - way. ___

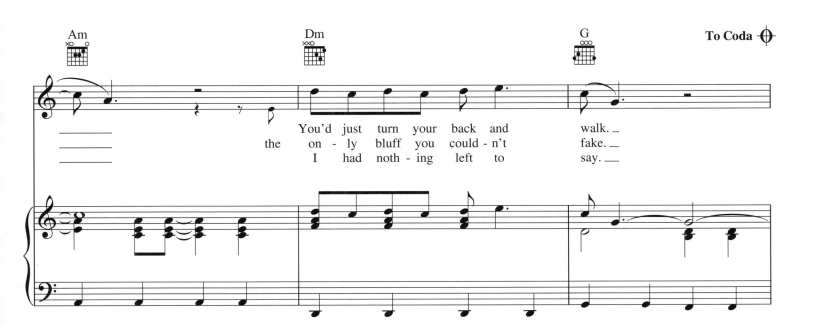

___
___ the on - ly bluff you could - n't
___ I had noth - ing left to

You'd just turn your back and walk. ___
fake. ___
say. ___

SWEET HOME ALABAMA

Words and Music by RONNIE VAN ZANT,
ED KING and GARY ROSSINGTON

I miss 'ole' 'bam - y once a - gain___ *(And I think it's a sin.)*

Verse

2. Well, I heard Mis - ter Young sing a -

bout her. Well, I heard ole Neil___ put her

down. Well, I hope Neil Young will re -

ADDITIONAL LYRICS

Verse 4. Now Muscle Shoals has got the Swampers
And they've been known to pick a tune or two
Lord they get me off so much
They pick me up when I'm feeling blue
Now how about you.

Repeat Chorus and Fade

THRILLER

Words and Music by
ROD TEMPERTON

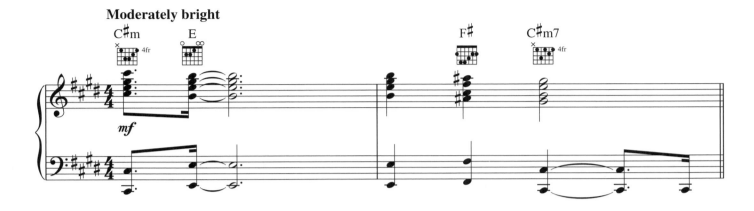

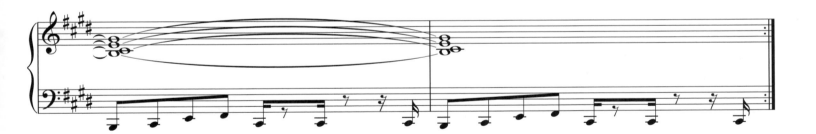

It's close to mid - night, and
You hear the door slam and
They're out to get you. There's

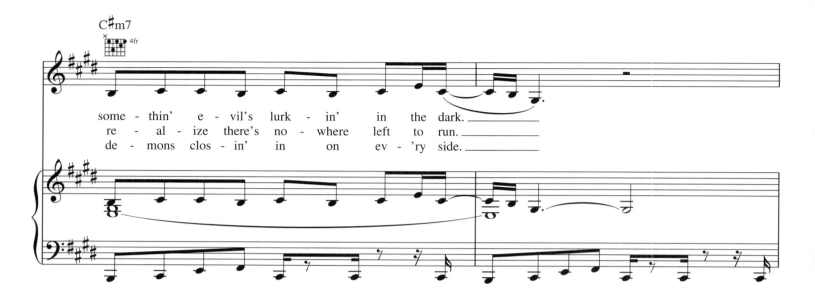

but ter - ror takes _ the sound _ be - fore _ you make _
and hope that this _ is just _ i - mag - i - na -
for you and I _ to cud - dle close _ to - geth -

_ it. _ You start to freeze _
- tion. _ But all the while, _
- er. _ All through the night _

as hor - ror looks _ you right _ be - tween _ the eyes. _
you hear the crea - ture creep - in' up _ be - hind. _
I'll save you from _ the ter - ror on _ the screen. _

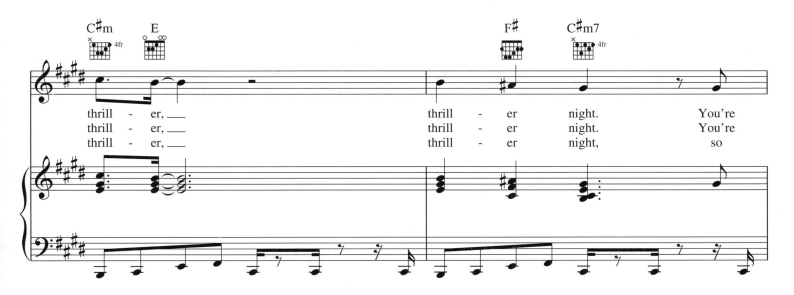

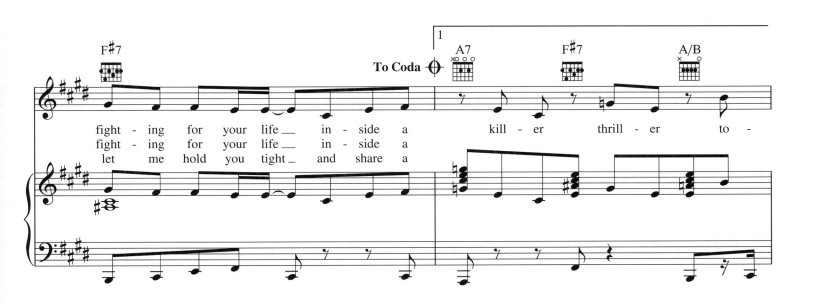

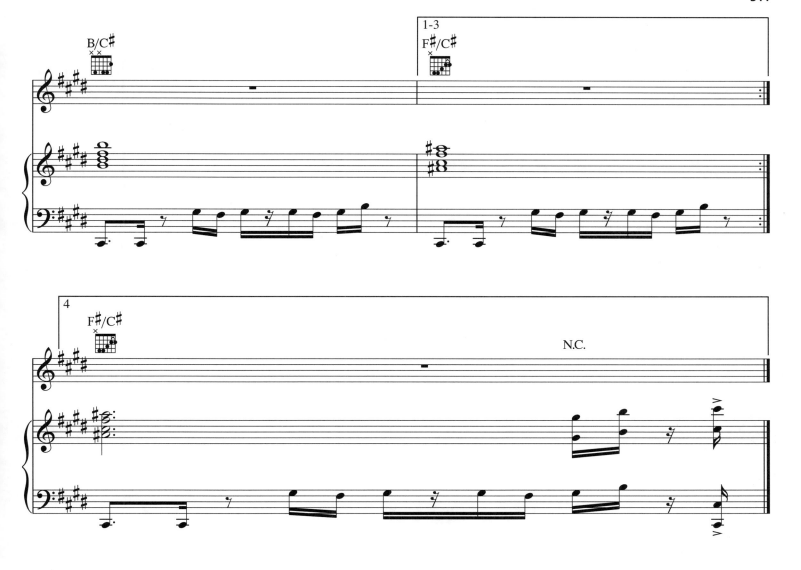

Spoken Lyrics

1. Darkness falls across the land.
   The midnight hour is close at hand.
   Creatures crawl in search of blood
   To terrorize y'all's neighborhood.
   And whosoever shall be found
   Without the soul for getting down
   Must stand and face the hounds of hell
   And rot inside a corpse's shell.

2. The foulest stench is in the air,
   The funk of forty thousand years,
   And grizzly ghouls from every tomb
   Are closing in to seal your doom.
   And though you fight to stay alive,
   Your body starts to shiver,
   For no mere mortal can resist
   The evil of a thriller.

TAKIN' CARE OF BUSINESS

Words and Music by
RANDY BACHMAN

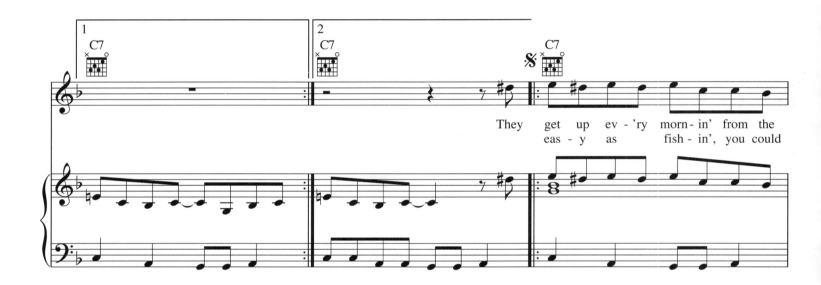

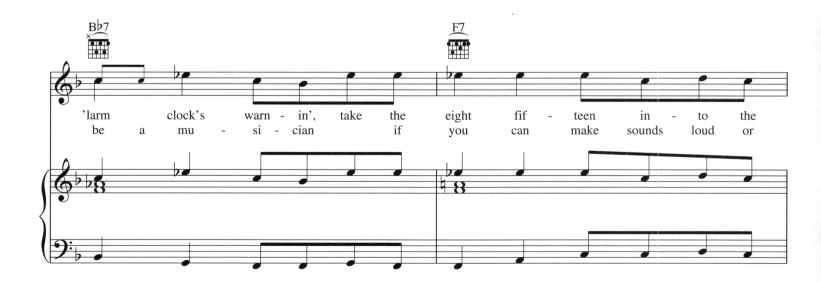

cit - y.
mel - low.

There's a whis - tle up a - bove and peo - ple
Get a sec - ond - hand gui - tar _____ chanc - es

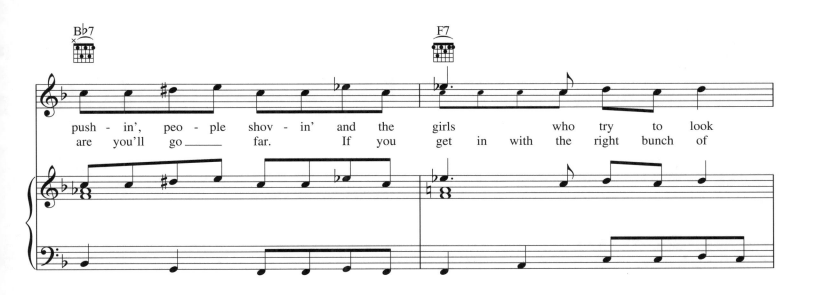

push - in', peo - ple shov - in' and the girls who try to look
are you'll go _____ far. If you get in with the right bunch of

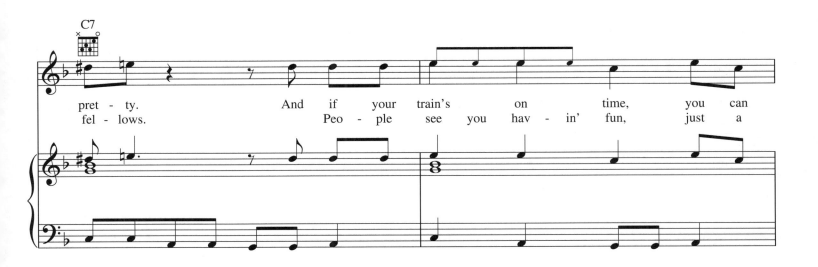

pret - ty.
fel - lows.

And if your train's on time, you can
Peo - ple see you hav - in' fun, just a

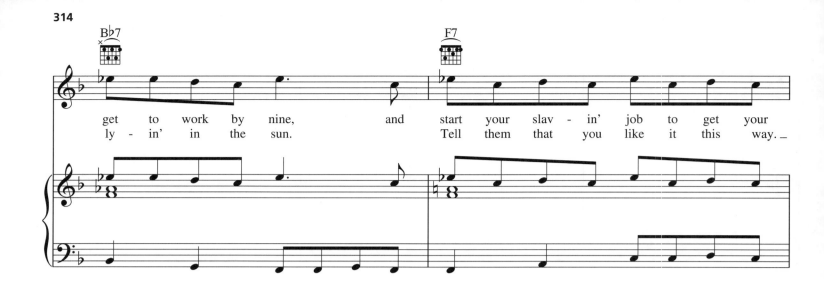

get to work by nine, and start your slav - in' job to get your
ly - in' in the sun. Tell them that you like it this way. —

pay.
— If you ev - er get an - noyed look at
It's the work that we a - void and we're

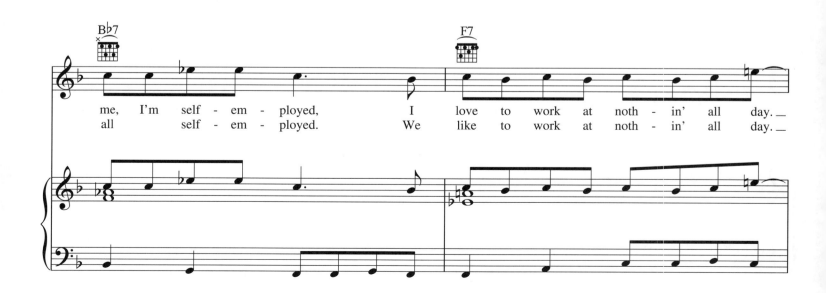

me, I'm self - em - ployed, I love to work at noth - in' all day. —
all self - em - ployed. We like to work at noth - in' all day. —

work - in' o - ver - time, work - out.
work - in o - ver - time.

There's work

UNDER THE BOARDWALK

Words and Music by ARTIE RESNICK
and KENNY YOUNG

Moderately, with a beat

Oh, when the sun beats down ____ and burns the
park you hear ____ the hap-py

tar up-on the roof, ____
sound of a car-ou-sel, ____

And your
You can

shoes get so hot you wish your tired feet ____ were fire -
al-most taste the hot-dogs and french-fries ____

WALK THIS WAY

Words and Music by STEVEN TYLER
and JOE PERRY

WALKING IN MEMPHIS

Words and Music by
MARC COHN

Walk - ing in Mem - phis but do I real - ly

feel the way __ I feel? __

They've __ got cat - fish on the ta -

- ble; __ they've __ got

WHATEVER GETS YOU THROUGH THE NIGHT

Words and Music by
JOHN LENNON

WRAPPED AROUND YOUR FINGER

Music and Lyrics by
STING

WHEEL IN THE SKY

Words and Music by ROBERT FLEISCHMAN, NEAL SCHON
and DIANE VALORY

Winter is here _____ a - gain _____ oh Lord
I been try - in' to make it home _____

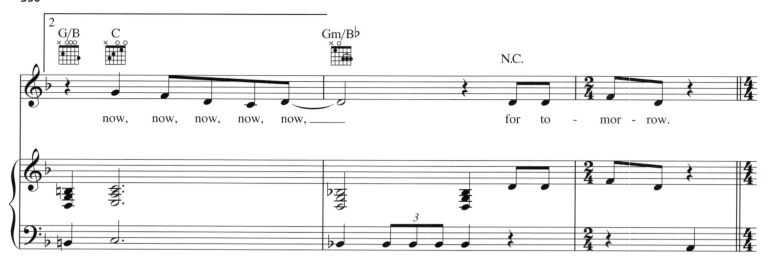

now, now, now, now, now, _____ for to - mor - row.

Guitar solo ad lib.

Play 3 times

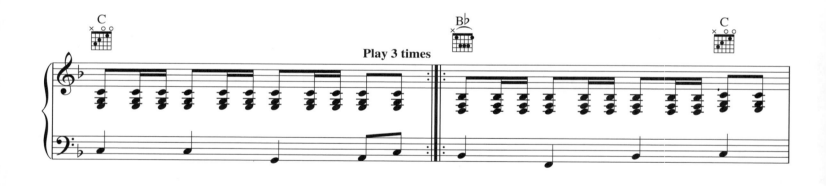

D.S. al Coda

Oh the

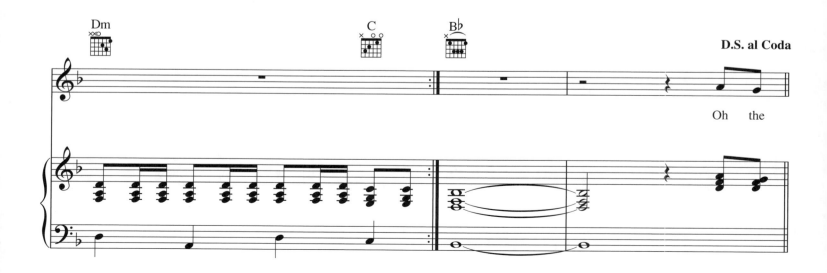

A WHITER SHADE OF PALE

Words and Music by KEITH REID
and GARY BROOKER

We skipped the light ____ fan - dan - go, ____
She said, "I'm home ____ on shore leave," ____
She said, "There is ____ no rea - son, ____

YOU REALLY GOT ME

Words and Music by
RAY DAVIES